Monster lives in a
house in the city.
He loves the house.
It's very, very fine.

He's got a bedroom,
a bathroom, a cupboard,
a living room and a kitchen.
It's very nice for a monster.
It's very comfortable.
Monster loves the house.

ALL ABOUT MONSTERS

4

He's reading a book about
monsters.
Because he's a monster himself,
he should read a monster book.

6

He thinks
he will clean the house
so that if children want to visit him
it will look really fine.

He cleans the bedroom.

If people come to stay he won't
have to clean the house
when they are sleeping.

He cleans the kitchen so that
when people come and want
to cook for monster they can.
The kitchen won't be all in a mess.

He cleans the bath so that when
people come in to have a bath
they won't get dirty.
When they pour the water in,
the water won't get dirty.

He cleans out the cupboard so
that people can put their clothes
inside and the clothes won't
get dirty.

Monster thinks he's done
enough cleaning.
He's very tired and sits down.
The house looks really fine.